LITTLE BOOK
········ OF ········
Bums

SADIE CAYMAN

summersdale

THE LITTLE BOOK OF BUMS

Summersdale Publishers Ltd
46 West Street
Chichester
West Sussex
PO19 1RP
UK

www.summersdale.com

Printed and bound in Malta

ISBN: 978-1-84953-907-4

Substantial discounts on bulk quantities of Summersdale books are available to corporations, professional associations and other organisations. For details contact Nicky Douglas by telephone: +44 (0) 1243 756902, fax: +44 (0) 1243 786300 or email: nicky@summersdale.com.

CONTENTS

INTRODUCTION

Oh yes! The backside is back. The butt is what's up. But don't call this a comeback – it's a renaissance! While society's obsession with bums seems like a thoroughly modern phenomenon, it can actually be traced back through art, poetry and writing to the dawn of humanity. We've always been a fan of some junk in the trunk. This little book traces the history of bottoms, takes a look at the science of the backside, notes the best exercises to tone the glutes, suggests a sweet-ass playlist and contains much more booty besides!

Bum
BASICS

Bone

You've (probably) been acquainted with your buttocks for the entirety of your life, but how well do you really know them? What's in a bottom? Would a bottom by any other name smell as sweet? It depends on the backside in question, but I digress. The building blocks of the butt start with the pelvis. It's one of the busiest junctions of the body, with the pelvic bone supporting the weight of the torso and the legs attaching via a ball-and-socket joint. The bits that give you your curves and swerves are called the ilium and the iliac crest. They are usually wider on a woman's pelvis than on a man's, as women's pelvises are broader in order to create a wider gap for any babies on their way out.

Bone

MALE PELVIS

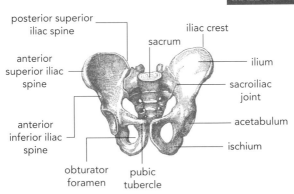

posterior superior iliac spine

anterior superior iliac spine

anterior inferior iliac spine

obturator foramen

pubic tubercle

sacrum

iliac crest

ilium

sacroiliac joint

acetabulum

ischium

FEMALE PELVIS

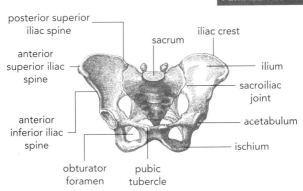

posterior superior iliac spine

anterior superior iliac spine

anterior inferior iliac spine

obturator foramen

pubic tubercle

sacrum

iliac crest

ilium

sacroiliac joint

acetabulum

ischium

Muscle

Here we get to the meat of the backside: the muscle! The main man in charge of the bottom is a muscle that sounds like it's named after a Roman emperor: gluteus maximus. Emperor Maximus has two lesser siblings, the gluteus medius and gluteus minimus. The maximus takes all the glory, as it is the muscle largely responsible for the look and shape of the butt, as well as supporting the torso. However, the medius and minimus are the foot soldiers of the backside, responsible for the majority of the leg movements. Sitting on top of the muscle is a layer of fat, known as subcutaneous fat. This is also responsible for the shape of the buttocks, as well as acting as padding and an energy reserve. These are the basics of the bottom, although they are all slightly different from person to person.

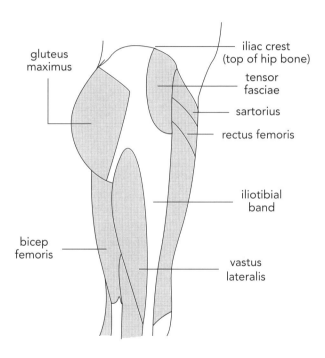

gluteus maximus

iliac crest (top of hip bone)

tensor fasciae

sartorius

rectus femoris

iliotibial band

bicep femoris

vastus lateralis

WHICH BUM ARE YOU?

Pear

Also known as: the 'A-shape' or 'heart-shaped' booty.
Check for: a waist that is considerably narrower than your hips and a bottom that is most fulsome towards the, er, bottom.

> → **Pros:** allegedly 'scientifically' the most attractive sort of backside, although we think all bottoms are covered with glory.
>
> → **Cons:** high-waisted shorts create a gappy circle of hell as your bum thinks you're one size and your waist is convinced you're another.

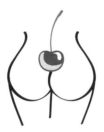

Cherry

Also known as: the 'bubble butt'
Check for: perfectly round, with the widest circumference in the middle.

→ **Pros:** pop culture loves a bubble butt! Just ask J-Lo.

→ **Cons:** your bum is so outwardly mobile that you need rear-view mirrors to avoid knocking it into people and fragile objects.

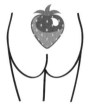

Strawberry

Also known as: the 'V-shape' buttocks.
Check for: a waist that is narrower than your hips, but also cheeks that taper or 'slant' inwards.

> • **Pros:** skinny-fit, boyfriend-fit, high-waisted, you can rock any shape of jeans!
>
> • **Cons:** you have to work extra hard to achieve a sufficiently percussive 'clap' when you're twerking.

Cake Slice

Also known as: the 'H-shape'.

Check for: a straight vertical line from waist to hip with no slanting (in or out!). If you trace the shape between the hips and the bottom of the cheeks, it would be square.

- **Pros:** tight and muscular, this is probably what Wonder Woman's bum looks like.

- **Cons:** without an abundance of nature's own cushions, long journeys can become uncomfortable.

Slang

Bum, butt, arse, backside – these are just a few of the commonly used words for your lower cheeks! But once you start to think of it, actually there are loads of weird and wonderful terms and euphemisms for bum. It makes you wonder if some people see bums wherever they go?

Caboose Hiney

Fanny Tush Tail

Rump Jacksie Trunk

Fundament Buns

Posterior Hams Booty

Peaches Badonkadonk

Chuff Patootie

SCIENCE IS RESPONSIBLE FOR MANY GREAT THINGS IN OUR LIVES FROM LIVING LONGER TO ADVANCED TECHNOLOGY, TO DRAMATIC COLUMN-FILLING STORIES IN THE TABLOIDS. BACON! IT GIVES YOU CANCER. RED WINE! IT REDUCES HEART DISEASE. LEFT-HANDED PEOPLE! THEY HAVE A SHORTER LIFESPAN. WE CAN THANK SCIENTISTS' INSATIABLE CURIOSITY AND SENSE OF 'NO RESEARCH IS TOO RIDICULOUS' FOR DISCOVERING THESE CONNECTIONS BETWEEN PAIRS OF SEEMINGLY RANDOM OBJECTS. SO WHAT HAS SCIENCE YIELDED IN ITS FORAY INTO BOTTOMS?

BIG BUTT EQUALS GOOD INTUITION

A US study found that women with low waist-to-hip ratios (in layman's terms that's a small waist and big hips) are better able correctly to read body language and facial expressions than women with a high waist-to-hip ratio. This means, among other things, that these women are better able to tell if someone is being dishonest and correctly asses the emotion another human is feeling based on their facial expression. The study had many potential explanations for this superior ability, including the theory that women with low waist-to-hip ratios are more likely to be targeted by dishonest partners, so have had to develop this intuitive ability in order to protect themselves. Ladies, if in doubt, trust what your butt is telling you.

Diagnosis bottom

LADY LUMPS ARE CAMEL HUMPS (SORT OF)

Telling someone that their bum is like a pair of camel's humps rarely goes down well, but this is serious! It doesn't mean that your bum grows and shrinks depending on the seasons and is surprisingly furry (although no judgement call were it to fulfil any of those criteria). Instead, this refers to the fact that your body burns fat reserves when it can't burn food and the bum is one of the key places your body stores fat – just like the camel's humps store fat for nourishment. In a way, with all that back-up energy in the form of fat, your butt is almost like a battery. It's a butt-ery!

Diagnosis bottom

SMART ARSES

As if pregnant women need anything else to worry about, a study released by the University of Pittsburgh claims that women with big thighs and buttocks have cleverer children. Or rather, the study discovered that around 80 per cent of an acid essential for the development of a baby's cognitive function is created by stored fat, primarily in a mother's thighs and bottom. This then gets transferred during the breastfeeding stage, which is part of the reason that a breastfeeding mother can lose up to a pound of fat a month.

ROBUTTOCKS

In 2012 a team of Japanese scientists unveiled their masterpiece: a set of robotic buttocks named Shiri. They were built to express the emotions fear, joy and relaxation. When you give them the appropriate stimuli – such as caressing them – they react in a human way – such as clenching in 'pleasure'. This experiment wasn't just for fun – the scientists saw this as the first step in creating realistic emotions in a whole different set of robotic cheeks, those of the face.

WOMBUTT

What's the coolest thing about a wombat? Is it their chubby bodies and little legs? That they can get up to speeds of 25 miles per hour? Or is it that they have a reinforced butt they use as a sort of shield to protect themselves? It's definitely the backside! Wombats have a unique layer of thick cartilage and skin protecting their rump; so in times of peril they can stand bum-out at the entrance to their burrow, protecting themselves and any young. Reportedly, their butt can be used to crush the skull of a fox or dingo attacking the burrow!

CHEEK AND CHEERFUL

Charles Darwin said this of the male mandrill, 'No other member in the whole class of mammals is coloured in so extraordinary a manner as the male mandrill.' This is pretty much the Victorian naturalist version of 'Oh my God Becky, look at her butt.' The violet-pink-and-blue colouration on the male mandrill's buttocks is believed to have two purposes: one is to show dominance – the more brightly coloured your bum is, the bigger boss you are –

and the second is to attract the ladies. After all, there's no gentleman like a gentleman with fluorescent cheeks, am I right girls?

EAU DE BUTT

There's nothing quite so tasty as the anal secretions of a beaver. Don't believe me? Just check the next bag of sweets that you're tucking into. The beaver has glands around its butt that secrete a substance called castoreum, a slimy brown substance that can be used for anything from vanilla or strawberry flavouring to perfumes and air fresheners. If you're trying to cut back on the treats, just think of the beaver's anal secretions and you might be put off.

Ah, humans. Our ingenuity, creativity, determination and occasional oddness have led us to places no other species could dream of. Possibly literally, as scientists aren't too sure what it is other species are dreaming about. Thanks to those qualities, humans fly in metal machines, can remove organs from their bodies and replace them with new ones and have touched the moon. Humans are constantly pushing themselves and inspiring themselves, gaining all sorts of achievements in all sorts of fields. Here are some choice achievements in the field of the butt:

The world record for largest bum (by circumference) as of 2015 is held by Mikel Ruffinelli, of the USA. She measures 8.25 ft around the hips and buttocks. In second place is Marlena Plummer, fellow US citizen, with a hip and buttock measurement of a mere 7 ft.

The gluteus maximus holds **the Guinness World Record for being the bulkiest muscle in the body**, beating the other 639 named muscles for the title. Although size varies from individual to individual, the average weight of the muscle is around 850 g. However, during pregnancy the uterus can challenge the glute's record, increasing from around 30 g to over 1 kg in weight (and that's without counting the baby inside of it). That's an increase of over 3,300 per cent.

In case you were wondering, the current **Guinness World Record for fastest 100-m bum walk** is 11 minutes and 59 seconds, held by Miki Sakabe of Japan since 2009. The race was witnessed by two officials from the Association of Hokkaido Field-and-Track events, which makes you wonder whether it was a nice day out for them or if they questioned the state of athletic competition today. If you'd like to see if you have what it takes to be a bum-walking champion, sit with your legs flat out in front of you, with no part of your arms or hands touching the floor to assist. Try it and see what your best time is!

The Guinness World Record for fastest 20-m bum scoot is held by an American, Samuel Jackson, and was achieved in 2013. It's a mere 20.31 seconds, so it seems bum scooting is a much faster mode of transportation than bum walking (if you needed to get somewhere in a hurry but would still like to use your butt as your primary mode of propulsion).

Bum
EXERCISES

THERE ARE LOTS OF GET-FIT-QUICK TIPS FLOATING ABOUT THAT PROMISE TO GIVE YOU KYLIE'S BOTTOM IN A MATTER OF DAYS, USUALLY INVOLVING THE WORDS 'CRUNCH', 'TONE' OR 'BURN'. IMPORTANT PUBLIC SERVICE ANNOUNCEMENT: IF ANY EXERCISE PROMISES TO BURN 'BOTTOM FAT', DON'T BELIEVE IT. FAT IS AN ENERGY RESOURCE PRESENT NEARLY ALL OVER THE BODY. WHEN YOU EXERCISE, THE BODY HAS NO WAY TO 'MATCH' THE AREA OF BODY BEING WORKED AND TAP INTO THE FAT HELD THERE. INSTEAD, ALL OF THE RESERVES OF FAT ARE USED; THE BODY VIEWS THEM AS ONE UNIFIED ENERGY SOURCE. IF YOU WANT TO TRULY 'TONE' AN AREA, THE WAY TO DO THAT IS TO TARGET AND DEVELOP THE MUSCLE OR MUSCLES THERE. HERE ARE A FEW EXERCISES THAT FOCUS ON BUILDING YOUR GLUTES AND DEVELOPING A STRONG BOTTOM!

WALL KICKS

You'll need some clear wall space handy for this easy exercise that targets the holy trinity of legs, bums and tums. You'll also need a reasonable balancing ability, but that will improve with time as your core strengthens and you get used to the exercise. If you're still worried, pile a few cushions up either side of you!

 Stand facing the wall, body relaxed and feet hip-width apart.

 Place your hands on the wall at shoulder height.

 Bend forward at the hips and extend your leg out behind you, bent at the knee.

 Bring your knee to your chest and then back out to the previous position.

 Repeat between 15 and 30 times on each leg. Two sets are recommended.

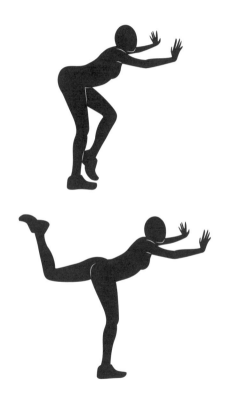

LEG EXTENDERS

Equipment-free and super easy to get the hang of, this is a classic exercise to work the glutes. Don't value pace over quality for this one – the slower the movement the stronger the muscles will get. However, to start it's better to be able to complete the sets than to burn out after two perfectly controlled extenders on each leg!

1 Starting position: on hands and knees with hands directly under shoulders and a flat back.

2 Move your left leg through and place your left foot by your hand, so you are in 'on your marks' position.

3 Extend the same leg out behind you, taking it as high as it will go.

4 Quickly bring your leg back to 'on your marks' position.

Repeat between 15 and 30 times on each leg. Two
sets are recommended.

········ *Exercises* ········

HEADS DOWN, BUMS UP

Just because this one is done lying down doesn't mean it's easy! This is one of the tougher exercises on the list. Building pure gluteal strength, it's a challenge where achievement is measured in inches rather than strides.

1 Lie down on your front with your arms folded under your head for support and your legs extended directly out behind you.

2 Bend one leg at the knee, keeping the knee on the floor. Place the foot of the bent leg on the back of the knee of the straight leg.

3 Without raising your hip (this will be harder than you expect), clench the buttock of the bent leg and lift that knee a few inches off the floor if you can.

4 Hold the knee in the air for a few beats and then release the buttock and return the knee to the floor. Repeat ten times then repeat on the opposite leg.

You can increase the number of reps as you improve.

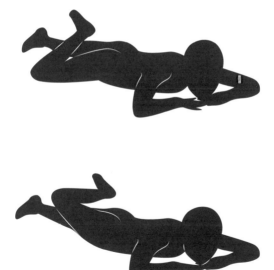

·········· Exercises ··········

PIGEON POSE

Flexibility is good for the backside. You want to have moves like Beyoncé? That's not just strength, girl, that's flexibility. Sure Beyoncé does her lunges but she's probably getting her yoga in too.* Try this pigeon pose for a deep, effective stretch that works all sorts of magic in your hips.

1 Sit with one leg folded in front of you as if you were going to 'cross legs' and the other leg stretched out directly behind you.

2 Relax your muscles so that your hips fully drop down and the cheek belonging to the folded leg is touching the floor.

3 If your cheek doesn't touch the floor, don't worry. This is perfectly normal for beginners and even for many long-time yoga practitioners – every body is different. In this case, insert something firm like a foam block or strong cushion underneath to support the muscle.

• • • • • • • • • • • • • • • • • • •

Keeping your chest lifted, hold the position for ten seconds to start. Repeat on the other side.

 To deepen the stretch, fold at the waist until your forehead is touching the floor and your arms are stretched out in front of you. For an expert-level stretch, bend the extended leg up at the knee and reach behind to hold that foot.

* The author would like to note that she has no actual knowledge of Beyoncé's exercise regime.

·········· Exercises ··········

WEIGHT UP!

A lot can be done to build muscle using only your body and some clear floor space. However, some exercises, such as this one, use props to take it to the next level. Start small when using weights for the first time; you want a pert bottom not a hurt bottom. If you don't own weights, start with two full water bottles.

 Stand behind a set of dumbbells, legs hip-width apart.

 Maintaining a flat back, squat and take hold of the dumbbells with an overhand grip. Your chest should be upright and over your knees.

Root your feet firmly into the ground and stand up, straightening your legs and unbending at the waist. Keep your arms straight and near your body.

Lower the dumbbells down with a flat back squat, as originally. Repeat for ten reps.

5 The gluteus maximus is primarily responsible for the movement of your torso at the waist, so this will be really working it.

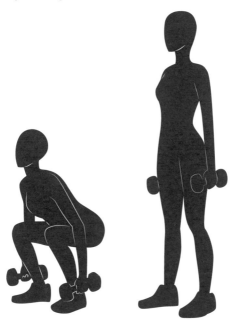

VIVE LA RESISTANCE

Another exercise that uses a prop, this time a resistance band. If you don't have one, do consider getting one; they're a very versatile bit of kit and not at all expensive. This is one to do in the really quiet moments – you don't want to forget you've secured your legs together then go running for the doorbell.

1 Secure the resistance band around your ankles so you have enough material to move your legs apart.

2 Plant one foot firmly on the ground and slide the other out to the side until you are creating tension in the material.

3 Hold the position for around ten seconds and then return your foot to the centre. Repeat on the other side for five sets.

GUIDE TO TWERKING

If a twerk is worth doing, it is worth doing well, as someone famous almost certainly never said. Still, if the squad have cleared the dance floor and you're in the middle, ready to blow the crowd away, it's probably a good idea to have at least some idea what you're about to do. It's no use feebly shaking your booty and calling it a twerk, it's time to officially wow the crowd. Here is a quick guide to mastering the most popular twerking styles.

SQUAT AND SHAKE

A good beginners' move to get you started. If you have space, try following the actions in front of a mirror (or a kind friend), so you have a good idea of what you're doing and how you're looking.

1 Stand with your legs wide apart, with your knees bent and feet turned out. Move down into a squat position, although you should not be too low to the ground in 'full' squat.

2 Lean forward at around a 45-degree angle (no need for a protractor!) and place your hands on your knees or hips. To achieve a nicely flexible twerk, your weight should be on your toes.

3 'Pop' your booty up and down, keeping the upper half of your body mostly still. A good way to do this is to arch and release your back in time with the bounce of your backside; this keeps the movement localised to your lower torso/bum/upper thigh area.

WALL TWERK

Perhaps not one for the centre of da club dancefloor, but pretty impressive nonetheless. Before you attempt this one in public, test it at home to see if you have ample arm muscles to support yourself. No one needs to be stretchered off the dancefloor!

1 Stand around two feet away from a wall. If you're feeling a little nervous, you can surround yourself with 'crash cushions' to break any potential falls, but leave some space in front of you. This is where your hands will go.

2 Put your hands flat on the floor and step your feet up the wall until your knees are bent and your toes are your body's highest point, then move your feet wide apart. You should basically be in the squat position of the previous twerk, but with the weight on your hands instead of your feet.

3 Ensure you are feeling secure and that you are able to maintain your position. Pop your junk up and down, using the same technique as described previously.

HANDS ON THE GROUND

Advanced-level twerking that depends at least a little bit on your pre-existing level of flexibility.

1 Stand with feet wide apart and, bending at the waist, put your hands flat on the floor. If you need to bend your legs a little to do this, do so.

2 Straighten your legs – ideally until they are completely straight but allow yourself a little bend if you need it.

3 Bend and straighten your legs in time with the beat. It has to be fairly quick – too slow and you'll look like you're warming up for a twerking session.

History
OF BUMS

ON THE ONE HAND, IT'S PRETTY EASY TO TRACE THE HISTORY OF BUMS IN MUCH THE SAME WAY AS IT'S EASY TO TRACE THE HISTORY OF ELBOWS OR THE HISTORY OF TOES. YOU FOLLOW THE HISTORY OF HUMANS BACK ALONG THE TIMELINE, JUMP OVER TO THE HISTORY OF PRIMATES, THEN MAMMALS AND THEN FINALLY END UP AT THE PART OF HISTORY WHERE THINGS STARTED CRAWLING OUT OF THE OOZE AND FIND THEMSELVES NEEDING USEFUL BITS LIKE ELBOWS AND TOES AND, INDEED, BUMS. HOWEVER, WE'RE INTERESTED IN HOW LONG WE'VE LOVED BUMS. WHEN DID OUR LOVE AFFAIR WITH BOTTOMS START? TURNS OUT, ACTUALLY, PRETTY MUCH STRAIGHTAWAY...

VENUS OF HOHLE FELS

This well-endowed woman was found in Schelklingen in Germany. She is only 6 cm tall and carved out of ivory from a woolly mammoth tusk. But most importantly, she was dated to around 35,000–40,000 years ago, to the Upper Palaeolithic period. She has big boobs, a large stomach and plenty of junk in her trunk, although she is sadly missing a head and some limbs. She was found near a bone flute, which is possibly the oldest musical instrument ever found, and has a perforation which may indicate she was worn as an amulet. So it seems as soon as humans turned their hand to carving, one of the first things on their mind was the butt!

VENUS OF WILLENDORF

A little younger than the Venus of Hohle Fels, at a mere 30,000 years old, and carved from limestone, for years this Venus was thought to be the oldest statue ever found and she still holds on to her title of oldest 'undisputed' statuette. You'll notice by now that despite these ladies appearing thousands of years before the myth of Venus or Aphrodite ever popped up, archaeologists seem pretty keen to slap the name 'Venus' on them. Originally, it was assumed that due to their generous

curves and the 'exaggerated' focus on parts of the body associated with child rearing, they could be totems representing fertility. However, a few theories now float the idea that they were simply a self-portrait – so maybe they are the world's first belfie (bum selfie!). It could be that all those 'exaggerated' curves were merely the images of the women making them.

HOTTENTOT VENUS

Another year, another Venus! This one isn't a statuette but a woman named Saartjie Baartman, born to the Khoikhoi tribe in what is now known as South Africa, around 1790. Her origins are somewhat obscured but it seems she was a slave of a Boer farmer and was sold to a travelling showman and exhibited around England and then Paris. She drew crowds because of her large buttocks and thighs, common to the women of her tribe and of surrounding areas in Africa, but alien to the Caucasian women of Europe. As if the indignity of being displayed wasn't enough, for an extra fee visitors could poke her with a stick. She was treated as a spectacle, dehumanised and manhandled by visitors. Scientific thinking at the time was that her physique, extraordinary to the western world, was an indication of 'primitivism' – something we know holds no water under scientific scrutiny today. However, something of the idea lingers with the insidious prejudice in popular culture that equates curves, especially those of a woman of colour, with promiscuity.

Here are some commonly used phrases that seem to be referring to the bum in some way – did they originate from somewhere sensible or did someone just pull them out their ass one day?

BUTTLOAD

Surprise, your snarky teenage self was right! A buttload is actually a recognised unit of measurement. However, it doesn't actually mean 'approximately the quantity of a big bum'. It comes from the Middle English *bote* and was used as a measurement of alcohol. It's not an old-school version of a single or double though. If you had a butt of alcohol in your mixer, it would be 491 litres (plus a splash of soda).

····· *Bum etymology* ·····

ASSLOAD

You guessed it! An assload is, again, nothing to do with bums. It is, instead, the amount a donkey, or ass, can carry. It was even used in the Bible (one assumes it was a precise unit of measurement in those days) and is meant to be roughly equivalent to 8 bushels.

Bum etymology

BUM AROUND

To 'bum around' means to wander aimlessly and was originally American slang. This grew out of the American term for tramps – bums – who wandered from town to town in search of income and employment. The term 'bum' doesn't refer to rear ends but instead probably developed from the German word *bummler*, meaning loafer. This, in turn, grew from the world *bummeln*, meaning 'to go slowly' or 'waste time'. Which is now what 'bum around' means. Phew – we've come full circle.

BLOWING SMOKE UP YOUR ARSE

As the old saying goes, it's not over until the doctor has attached a tube and handheld bellows to your bottom and puffed smoke up your jacksie. In the 1700s, unsuspecting victims of drowning would be hauled out of the water and, if they were unconscious or possibly dead, doctors would go through the aforementioned hullabaloo in an attempt to resuscitate them. If that didn't work, the final option would be to attempt artificial respiration. Of course, that was only in really desperate circumstances.

Mouth to mouth? Eurgh! Tube to bottom? Much preferred! Although the process has died out (we discovered tobacco had those pesky side effects) the phrase 'blowing smoke up someone's arse' has lingered as a term for a person who is saying something complimentary in an insincere manner.

Bum etymology

AMERICA VS ENGLAND

Pavement versus sidewalk, trousers versus pants, aubergine versus eggplant; many tiny battles rage between parent language English and its errant child, American English. Of all these clashes of truth and justice, surely the least terrible is arse versus ass (the most terrible is spring onions versus scallions. It sounds as though someone has named the spring onion after a particularly cheeky child). After all, it's merely a matter of accent, is it not? You say ass, I say arse, let's call the whole thing off? Actually, the crack between the two words runs deeper than that; ass and arse are born of completely different roots! You can trace the history of ass back to the Romans, and the Latin word *asinus*, while arse is derived from Old English *aers*. *Asinus* makes the whole affair sound quite dignified, whereas if you pronounce *aers* in the Old English fashion ('ae' as in the a in 'cat' and the other letters as modern pronunciation) one sounds like a bad Father Jack impersonator.

Butt crime

Sadly, sometimes the phrase 'she had a bum to die for' rings all too true. And sometimes there isn't an appropriate saying to sum up quite what these cheeky criminals were up to.

CAUGHT RED... CHEEKED?

In Valentine, Nebraska, businesses were being targeted by a horrific crime… Someone had been leaving greasy bum prints on their storefront windows. The 'attacks' continued for at least a year before the culprit was caught – their MO was apparently to apply lotion to their buttocks in order to leave a visible mark. Police were reportedly relieved to catch the criminal as they had feared a spate of copycat crimes breaking out. Maybe frosted glass would have become popular in the area?

OH NOSE!

A member of staff at a Plymouth Co-op had a brush with the unexpected when a customer was caught sniffing his bum on CCTV. The victim had suspected something strange had been going on while he was stacking shelves but wasn't sure until he asked his manager to review the security footage. It showed not one but two visits from the bottom-sniffer, who would pretend to be browsing groceries only to suddenly kneel down for a whiff. Although the police released the footage and asked for anyone with information to come forward, the perpetrator is still at large.

TED BUNDY'S BUTT BITE

Serial killer Ted Bundy may have gotten away with it all if it hadn't been for the bite mark on the buttock of one of his last victims. Charismatic and incredibly careful when committing his crimes, by 1977 he had already escaped jail in Aspen, where he was being held during his trial for murder. In January of 1978 he killed two sorority girls, one of whose buttocks he bit. It was the buttock that held the key to his conviction for murder as prosecutors were able to link the teeth marks to Bundy's own gnashers, one of the only bits of physical evidence linking Bundy to any crime.

Shakespearean insults

Old Shakey shaped the way we talk about love, about life and death, about nature – about everything really. He has become a byword for culture and the art of language. As it happens, he was also the king of the sick burn. There was no low that Shakespeare would not stoop to. He varied from the bizarre – *thou thimble!* – to the really quite hurtful – *Thou art a boil, a plague sore, an embossed carbuncle*. Well shucks, Shakespeare, there's no need to be like that. With such an impressive range, it's no surprise that he managed to touch upon the butt every now and then. So without much further ado, here are two top Shakespearean insults and possibly the first ever 'What type of bum are you?' list in history.

YOU RUINOUS BUTT.

TROILUS AND CRESSIDA

YOUR BUM IS THE GREATEST THING ABOUT YOU.

MEASURE FOR MEASURE

IT IS LIKE A BARBER'S
CHAIR THAT FITS
ALL BUTTOCKS;
THE PIN-BUTTOCK,
THE QUATCH-BUTTOCK,
THE BRAWN-BUTTOCK,
OR ANY BUTTOCK.

ALL'S WELL THAT ENDS WELL

Bums
IN CULTURE

AS THE POET BUBBA SPARXX ONCE SAID, 'BOOTY BOOTY, ROCKIN' EVERYWHERE'. POP CULTURE LOVES ITSELF SOME BUMS, AND SOME PEOPLE CAN BUILD CAREERS ON THE CURVE OF THEIR DERRIÈRE. IT ISN'T JUST POP CULTURE EITHER – SOME OF THE WORLD'S FINEST ART HAS BEEN INSPIRED BY SOME OF THE WORLD'S FINEST REAR ENDS. LESS GENDER-SPECIFIC THAN BOOBS AND LESS RUDE THAN GENITALIA, BUMS ARE THE WORLD'S FAVOURITE NAUGHTY BIT!

Playlist

Whether you're going out, working out or vegging out, you're in need of a sweet-ass playlist to set the mood. Or, in this case, a sweet playlist about asses:

'SHAKE YOUR BOOTY'
KC and the Sunshine Band

Start with this smooth disco-era booty shaker – the perfect background tune for shimmying across the room for your make up, shimmying across the room to get your weights or shimmying across the sofa to get your next snack.

'ORIGINAL RUMP SHAKER'
Wreckx-n-Effects

From the golden age of disco to the golden age of hip hop. Like Wreckx-n-Effects, when it comes to the backside, sometimes all you want to do is a zoom zoom zoom zoom.

Playlist

'BOOTYLICIOUS'
Destiny's Child

Pick up the pace a little and start to strut with this thrumming celebration of your body, your butt and most especially yourself.

'MY HUMPS'
The Black Eyed Peas

Continue the self-love as Fergie describes the many bountiful benefits her 'asstributes' have brought her in life.

'ANACONDA'
Nicki Minaj

If anyone knows a thing or two about loving herself and her booty, it's Miss Nicki Minaj. Turn it up a notch with this bombastic banger punctuated with samples from the titan of butt songs, 'Baby Got Back'.

Playlist

'AZZ EVERYWHERE'
Big Freedia

It's not surprising that the queen of New Orleans bounce and twerking Guinness-world-record-holder Big Freedia has released one of the most joyful songs about a club full of butts.

'BABY GOT BACK'
Sir Mix-a-Lot

Oh my God Becky, this is the ultimate in songs about bums. Sir Mix-a-Lot is so happy and celebratory of big butts that you can't help but stop what you're doing and shake it, wherever you are.

'FAT BOTTOMED GIRLS'
Queen

The track listing reached its booty-shaking-climax with Sir Mix-A-Lot but who better to bring it home than the kings of the end-of-the-night tune, Queen? It's time to grab a friend and wail to the world how fat bottomed girls make the rocking world go round (yeah).

Bums in film

REAR PIONEER

The first bare-bottom featured in a moving picture was French (of course it was) and belonged to actress Jehanne d'Alcy. She featured in 1897 in a one-minute film titled *After the Ball*, in which she disrobed, back and backside to the camera, and was bathed by a servant. Racy stuff! In an excellent meeting of old and new technologies, it is available to watch on YouTube.

NO. 4

Among Yoko Ono's many experimental art pieces is a 1967 short film titled *No.4*, but more often referred to as *Bottoms*. There are no prizes for guessing the subject of the film; for five and a half minutes cameras track humans walking on treadmills, in a series of butt-based close ups. The glass eyes are so close to the bums that the screen is almost perfectly divided into four – down the middle by the gluteal cleft, and horizontally by the gluteal crease. The film had at least one superfan; in 1996 Swatch produced a watch commemorating the film.

Insurance

J-LO

If you had a career-making booty, wouldn't you want to lock down your assets? Jennifer Lopez is rumoured to have insured her bum for millions, so should anything unfortunate happen to it (presumably more serious than pulling a muscle) she is set for a payout. To add more rumour beans to the rumour mill, the figure is reckoned to be anything between $27 million and $300 million. How much do you think you could secure your cheeks for? The price of a chocolate bar?

JOHN ABRAHAM

J-Lo isn't alone: Bollywood actor John Abraham had his cheeks (lower) insured for ten million rupees, otherwise known as £1.35 million. Body insurance is less common in Bollywood than Hollywood and this made quite the stir when it came to light. Still, if your booty is making bank, it makes sense to keep that money coming in.

SUZANNA

Brazilian Playmate Suzanna has also insured her bum for $2 million, in a policy that also strangely covers her ankles and knees but not any other part of her leg. This was a publicity stunt for the insurer and the pin-up appeared on billboards advertising the deal. Allegedly, securing insurance for your butt has become so common in Brazil that Brazilians have a name for it – a 'Bum bum policy'. Zero points for creativity, although some points for an unusual trend.

Bums in the Arts

From the *Venus Callipyge* to Kim Kardashian's *Paper* cover, bottoms have held a special place throughout the history of art. Sculpted, photographic or in pen and ink, the bottom can be a symbol of social satire as easily as it can be a visual ideal.

VENUS CALLIPYGE

Venus Callipyge literally translates to 'Venus of the beautiful buttocks'. And boy does she know it; the statue of Venus peers over her shoulder, skirts swept to the side, to admire her beautiful marble behind. This Roman sculpture is supposedly based on an older Greek statue of mysterious origin. There are old legends that a pair of beautiful sisters demanded a stranger tell them who had the more stunning rear – their charming cheeks eventually brought prosperity to the city and the citizens dedicated a temple to them!

THE MILLER'S TALE

Absolon, the parish clerk, comes a cropper in this Medieval classic from Chaucer. He falls in love with a fair young woman, the wife of the town miller, and sets to wooing her. Unfortunately her affections are set elsewhere and poor Absolon gets rather a bum deal. He comes to her window one night to steal a kiss and is tricked into kissing the fundament instead of the face. It's not clear how he didn't immediately clock that one, but the goggles of love can transform all sorts of faults.

'LECK MICH IM ARSCH'

I BEG your PARDON, Mozart? I thought you were a child prodigy and one of the greatest composers of our time?! And yet you've written a song about… I mean I don't speak German but the words are pretty similar to the English. However, Mozart's gotta Mozart – and this was more than just a silly little ditty: Wolfgang's version is a rather melodious canon round for six voices, in B-flat major.

· · · · · · · · · *Fame* · · · · · · · · · ·

KIM KARDASHIAN

The doyenne of ass-related fame, the unstoppable Kim K, has built a multi-million career for herself and her family almost solely on the power of her rear end. Love her or hate her, you have to be impressed by a woman who can make such a mountain out of a pair of molehills.

Asschievement: 'breaking the internet' with her nude cover of *Paper* magazine.

JENNIFER LOPEZ

Actress, singer and A-list bottom owner J-Lo was a proud big-posterior possessor in a time when the fashion was to have a tiny everything. However, that time is long behind us now. She now holds the position of grande dame of celebrity bums, still winning 'World's Best Celebrity Behind', whilst also continuing to be a multi-faceted, highly talented entertainer.

Asschievement: wearing *that* translucent, brown dress to the London *Maid in Manhattan* premiere. If they say eyes are the window to the soul, that fabric was the window to her underwear.

BEYONCÉ

Before twerking, the dance move we were all attempting (and failing) to recreate was Beyoncé's booty shake in her video for 'Crazy in Love'. At one time quite the daring dance move, now you're just pleased if you see your parents attempting that instead of a full-on twerk at the family party.

Asschievement: creating a song it is physically impossible not to shake your hips to with 'Crazy in Love'.

NICKI MINAJ

Just when it seemed the field of music inspired by the joy of bottoms would be dominated by men, Nicki Minaj arrived. Sharp tongued and shooting from the hip (and ass), the rap star's own booty is a favourite lyrical subject in both her own work and her guest verses.

Asschievement: breathing new life into the grandaddy of butt-based songs with her single 'Anaconda', Nicki is as jubilant to have a big ass as Sir Mix-a-Lot is to behold one.

PIPPA MIDDLETON

More of a one-hit wonder than a consistent player on the celebrity bum roster, it's pretty likely that the royal bridesmaid didn't expect to create a water cooler moment when she walked down the aisle for her sister's wedding. Still, you can't keep a good butt down and as she sashayed along the royal aisle, a moment was indeed created.

Asschievement: somehow managing to overshadow an entire royal wedding, for which the country was all but standing still, using the power of a single body part.

Bum fashions

Sometimes a celebrity gets accused of padding their butt out, or even having fillers, and things get a little tetchy. However, there was a time when ladies were affixing all sorts of contraptions to their backsides to create the most dramatic butt silhouette ever. By the time the Victorian era rolled around, the fashion industry and the Industrial Revolution had collided and bustles became hi-tech underwear.

1850s

Crinolines had been around for a while, but the shape was usually circular, so the skirt swept evenly around the body. In the 1850s, crinoline smoothed out at the front and sides and started to be all booty in the back, creating a butt-focused silhouette.

Crinolines had their dangers. They created such a large unwieldy skirt that the wearer often came to grief while trying to navigate everyday life. They were highly flammable, with several records of death by immolation caused by the wearer venturing too close to a fire in a crinoline. They were often very wide and could get caught underfoot or even under the wheel of a carriage. They could also get picked up by a gust of wind and upend the wearer, although this sounds less life-threatening and more hilarious (to the onlookers, at least).

1870s

The bustle arrived! This was a smaller contraption that wasn't so unwieldy; it no longer swept down to extend out the skirt but simply sat over the bottom to create a fuller figure. They came in many guises: some were horsehair ruffles that added padding, some were stiff braided wire that created specific shapes –

····· *Bum fashions* ·····

a sort of choose-your-booty situation – and others were surprisingly practical! The 'folding' bustle was advertised as 'light, cool and comfortable' – presumably for the fashionable woman on the go.

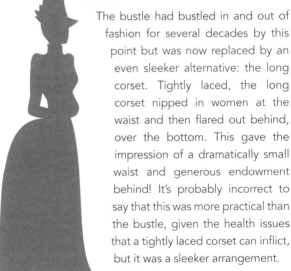

1900s

The bustle had bustled in and out of fashion for several decades by this point but was now replaced by an even sleeker alternative: the long corset. Tightly laced, the long corset nipped in women at the waist and then flared out behind, over the bottom. This gave the impression of a dramatically small waist and generous endowment behind! It's probably incorrect to say that this was more practical than the bustle, given the health issues that a tightly laced corset can inflict, but it was a sleeker arrangement.

Bustles to pads

1940s-50s

Crinolines had crept back in as part of the Dior 'New Look', although these were a return to the round hoop of yesteryear rather than the booty-bumping shapes of the 1850s. However, if you were going for a sleeker outfit, corsets and girdles would pull you in while hip padding would push you back out again in all the right places. Hip padding is still being used today, when stars want to get the right silhouette.

FEELING HOT-HOT-HOT PANTS

A couple of designers have garnered credit for the invention of hot pants; British designer Mary Quant is synonymous with the rising hemlines of the late 1960s and early 1970s, while Italian designer Mariuccia Mandelli cut very short shorts in her 1971 collection. Hot pants have come and gone over the years but one thing remains the same: outrage over just how high those hemlines are. From the town ordinances of the 1950s slapping a fine of $10 for anyone in too short shorts to fraught *Telegraph* headlines of today asking 'Men's shorts: how short is too short?'

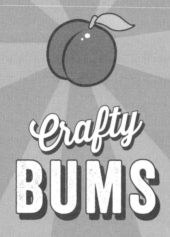

AS WE HAVE SEEN, FAMOUS WRITERS AND ARTISTS, FROM HISTORY TO THE MODERN DAY, HAVE DEDICATED THEMSELVES TO CREATING AMAZING WORKS BASED ON THE BUTT. AS I ALWAYS SAY, IF IT'S GOOD ENOUGH FOR SHAKESPEARE, IT'S GOOD ENOUGH FOR ME. IF YOU DON'T FANCY WRITING YOUR OWN SONNET ABOUT THE FABULOUSNESS OF YOUR BACKSIDE AND YOUR SHIPMENT OF MARBLE HASN'T ARRIVED IN TIME FOR YOU TO CARVE YOUR 'LIKENESS', TRY SOME OF THESE EASY AND FUN BUM-THEMED CRAFTS.

BUTTCAKES

Make this cake shaped like a butt for a special occasion, or to take into work for a company treat (note from editor: don't do that unless your colleagues are very open-minded). It's super cute and lots of fun to make.

INGREDIENTS

For the cake:
200 g caster sugar
200 g butter
4 eggs
200 g self-raising flour
1 tbsp baking powder
2 tbsp milk

For the filling:
Buttercream icing
Jam, flavour of your
  choice

For the topping:
Flesh-coloured
  fondant icing
Fondant icing, colour of
  your choice

1   Preheat the oven to 190 degrees Celsius. Beat the cake ingredients together until smooth, ensuring you have no lumps of butter or flour.

2   Line two 20-cm circular cake tins with greaseproof paper. Pour in the mixture and bake for 20 minutes or until golden. Test the cake is done by inserting a skewer in the centre – if it comes out clean, it's cooked.

3   When cake is cooled, trim into a heart shape. You may prefer to use a heart-shaped tin to start with.

Spread a layer of buttercream on one cake and a layer of jam on the other and then press together.

 Cover your now-combined cake in a thin layer of buttercream, in order to secure the fondant.

Sprinkle your worktop with icing sugar and roll out a circle of flesh coloured fondant, large enough to cover your cake on top and on the sides. Carefully lift and press to the cake. Trim any excess.

You now have a bare-bottom cake, with the rounded tops of the heart acting like cheeks. Here's where you can get creative. Use fondant icing to create jeans or trousers or even pants. To get the best effect, make sure the 'clothing' covers the side of the cake.

PADS

Believe it or not, not every celebrity is gifted with the perfect body. Lots of celebrities use subtle padding beneath their clothing to give the illusion of dramatic curves. Pads don't have to be used just for beauty though – these are perfect as a base for fancy dress, such as for a Jessica Rabbit costume.

You Will Need:

CLING FILM, SHARPIE PEN, MIRROR, SCISSORS, CARD, TWO LARGE FOAM PADS, BREAD KNIFE

Make

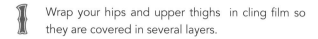

1 Wrap your hips and upper thighs in cling film so they are covered in several layers.

2 In front of a mirror, outline your bum cheek and upper thigh on each side.

3 Cut yourself free from the cling film (carefully – be kind to your curves!), then cut out your shapes. These will be the start of your moulds.

4 On the card, draw around your cling film shapes. This gives you a stiffer stencil, which will be easier to draw around on the foam.

5 Draw around your stencils on the foam, then cut out the shapes with the bread knife.

6 Using the knife, cut the edge off one side of the foam pad. This will become the side that gives you your curves. Still using the knife, create a long sloped edge. Leave a small flat 'island' in the middle.

7 Using the scissors, trim your pads into domes. The more dramatic your sloping, the more unrealistic and cartoonish your hips and buns will appear. Consider your costume, if these are for fancy dress.

8 When you are happy with the shape of your curves, stop snipping! These are now ready to be slipped under a pair of tights or two. Because your pads may be a little lumpy, doubling or even tripling up on your tights will give you a smoother silhouette.

DENIM HOT PANTS

A summertime classic, there's nothing like the combination of hot pants, trainers and a 99 ice cream. Revitalise an old pair of jeans with this easy upcycle.

You will need:

OLD OR SECOND-HAND JEANS, SHARPIE PEN, FABRIC SCISSORS, BRIGHT OR PATTERNED COTTON FABRIC, SEWING MACHINE

Make

1. Wearing the jeans, measure on your leg where you would like your hot pants to stop and then mark around 2 inches longer than that. The extra length will allow you to turn up the bottoms of the short to show off your fabric cuffs.

2. Remove the jeans and cut into shorts. Turn inside out. On the fabric, measure and mark a strip that is roughly 3 inches wide and will reach around the leg to overlap slightly.

3. Hem the fabric on both long edges. Align with the bottom of the short leg, so the fabric overhangs by around a half an inch, and pin in place. Sew the fabric around each.

4. Turn the shorts the right way round! Tuck and pin the overhanging fabric then sew it on to the outside of the short, creating a neat hem for your cuffs.

5. Fold up the end of your shorts about an inch to create showy fabric cuffs. If you want to customise further, try getting a retro iron-on patch to jazz up your bum pocket.

BUTTBREAD

The ultimate tear 'n' share, this basic bread recipe is good for not only a good loaf, but a good laugh.

Cook

INGREDIENTS

500 g strong white flour, plus extra for dusting
2 tsp salt
7 g sachet fast-action yeast
3 tbsp olive oil
300 ml water

> **Note:** this recipe requires a deep
> pan suitable for oven use.

1 In a large bowl, stir together the flour, salt and yeast. Create a well in the mixture and add the oil and water, mixing together well.

2 Once the ingredients are combined, lightly flour a work surface. Knead; if the dough is slightly dry or stiff you may need to return it to the bowl and add a tablespoon of water. Once the texture of the dough is smooth, lightly oil a bowl and place inside.

Leave in a warm, dry area of the house for one hour or until doubled in size.

 Pre-heat oven to 220 degrees Celsius. Split the dough into two and gently mould into two balls. Place in cast iron pan suitable for oven baking .

Dust the loaf with flour, place a lid on the pan and bake for 25–30 minutes until the loaves have fused together and are golden brown. Tip out and cool on a wire rack. When cool you will have the perfect cheeky snack for an evening of nibbles and giggles.

BUSTLE PILLOW

If you're looking to hustle for your own bustle, this pad is a great starter craft. It gives a little bump to your behind and is great for a late-Victorian fancy dress outfit.

You will need:

I-M-SQUARE FABRIC, I-M RIBBON, PEN, PAPER, PILLOW FIBRE OR RAGS, FABRIC SCISSORS, NEEDLE, THREAD, PINS

········ *Make* ········

1   On the paper draw a semicircle 35 cm wide and 17 cm deep. The final pillow should, when stuffed, be roughly as wide as your waist so if you'd like to adjust the measurements to fit, measure the width of your waist and add around 7 cm to allow for padding.

2   Cut out the template. Double up your fabric and pin the template along the folded edge, then cut along the template.

3   Measure and cut the length of ribbon required to tie firmly but comfortably around your waist. Open your folded semicircle and pin along one side of the fold, sewing in place.

4   Fill the ribboned side of the circle with pillow fibre, enough to create a substantial pillow but not so much that you can't close and sew the fabric over it. Pin the edges together and sew shut.

5   Wear under a sweeping skirt (if you want it to look good. Wear over a skirt if you want to look mildly odd).

BUTT CHALLENGE!

To break the ice, there's nothing like an easy word game that gets the creative juices flowing and allows you to be brilliantly silly. This quick-fire pun challenge isn't for the first time you meet the in-laws but will do quite nicely at a party for friends. Prizes are optional, although the gift of a brilliant pun is worthy by itself. Simply pick a topic – anything from a sweeping selection such as 'music' to a narrower category, such as James Bond films. Here are a few ideas to get you started:

······· *Challenge* ·······

MUSIC

Ludwig von Butthoven
Ass C/DC
Sergeant Pepper's Lonely Heart's Bum Band
Assputin
Dark Side of the Moon
Vanilla Arse

BOOKS

The Bum Also Rises
And Then There Were Bums
Pride and Prejud-ass
To Kill a Mockingbutt
David Cop a Feel
The Three Assketeers

FILMS

The Man with the Golden Buns
Invasion of the Botty Snatchers
Booty and the Beast
Star Wars: The Empire Strikes Back(side)

Jot your ideas here!

....
....
....
....
....
....
....
....
....
....
....
....
....
....
....
....
....

If you're interested in finding out more
about our books, find us on Facebook at
SUMMERSDALE PUBLISHERS and follow us
on Twitter at @SUMMERSDALE.

WWW.SUMMERSDALE.COM